HER(E)

A Collection of Queer Caribbean LGBTI Affirming Poems and Short Stories

Lysanne Charles

The short stories in this book are primarily works of fiction. Names, characters, places and incidents are the products of the author's imagination or are used fictitiously. Any resemblance to actual events, locales, or persons, living or dead, is entirely coincidental. The poetry may or may not have been inspired by true events.

 Published on Saba/St. Maarten, Dutch Caribbean by ZamiZemiPress a subsection of ZamiZemiProprietorship

ISBN I

1. LGBTI – Poetry 2. LGBTI – Fiction 3. Caribbean – Fiction

The author is committed to the empowerment of LGBTI persons across the Caribbean region and the continuing education about the intersection of issues; including environmental impacts. In this light the author and publishing house makes every attempt to use recycled products.

Printed in the United States of America by CreateSpace

978-99904-5-159-7

First edition

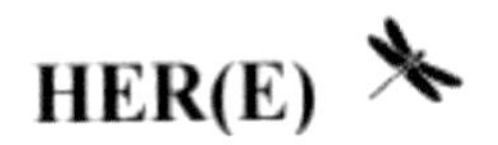

Book conceptualized by Lysanne Charles, edited by Dr. Maria van Enckevort, laid out by Alston Lourens/Lysanne Charles & book cover designed by Lincoln Charles and created by Danielle Fortune - Boodoo. Illustrations commissioned from Danielle Fortune - Boodoo.

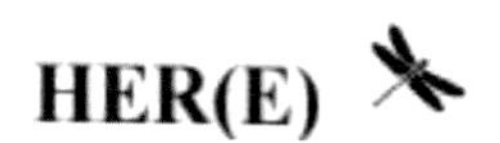

Dedication

To the rainbow and rainbow allied Warrior Women who went before me, those rainbow and rainbow allied warrior women who walk with me and those rainbow women and their allies still to come.

Acknowledgements

With great respect to my mother, grandmothers, great grandmother who loved me as I came and my great grandmother and great great grandmothers, who I never met, but who inspired me all the same.

Also to the women I have had the honor of loving and being loved by throughout my life thus far and to the woman who stood by my side throughout the drafting and completion of this book; love, light and gratitude always.

table of contents

foreword

I have spent the better part of the day clearing my mind to allow my impressions of my time with you to have free reign. The thing that stands out most is the first time I ever heard you recite poetry. I did not know you at all, but from the first delivery, from the tone of your voice, the level of depth, of realness, the actual words coming out of your belly, I knew I would work with you. I just said to myself 'I am going to work with her'; in what capacity I gave no thought, but I knew with a matter of certainty, with a matter of fact, that we would work together one day.

I had just come home from being submerged in the artist world of Jamaica and just a month before that the intense experience of being in South Africa, so my body was used to a certain level of profound artistry. When I saw you perform, I was pleased to know that right here in St. Maarten, I was able to find a continuation of that level of artistry and know that I could find compatible energy to connect with as an artist. I remember the words unfolding and feeling as if I had written them myself or that you had written them for me. I can still see you there standing in the limited light of the cultural center; you seemed golden and so full and vibrant, expressing with a dense truth your words; and importantly I can remember still the imagery that those words evoked in me.

Over the years, and many poems later, I am still moved each time another set of poems are released from you. They continue to possess their own depth, their own vastness and their own rhythms. The words put together in their own formation, sounds as if every word spoken was being said for the first time, as if every sentence and thought were new to the universe. There is no regurgitation of sentences, no repetition of tried and true clichés, and no funny, strange poet voice; there is just you, speaking from a deep place that resounds with my life's rhythm, with me and with many in your audiences.

I always wonder if my dancing body expressed the same profundity as expressed in your word flow. Was my dancing body expressing that complexity and newness that I heard each time I heard your words? Did my dancing body make people stop and reconsider things as your words did? Did my dancing body also give me permission to dream the way your poems allowed me to dream?

I know that being in this part of the world as a young artist, still in many ways trying to figure how to be an artist at home in the Caribbean, while trying to honor both our ancestors' voices and your own truth, has not been an easy journey. I know that you have done your best to try to respect the important the truth(s) of our craft without question, while battling self-doubt and insecurities about who you are as an artist. We have had many conversations about what our roles should be. Being able to bounce ideas off on each other, about who the voices that we were and are hearing and honoring and giving expression to are, has been a great honor for me and I hope it has been the same for you.

Over time, I have experienced your life's rhythm in the arts and it has been satisfying to watch you grow; knowing that your quest for excelling and revealing through words the inner landscape of our lives is constant. Knowing that despite being in and a part of this sun drenched paradise you still reveal that which needs revealing, that you awaken that which needs to be awakened and that you challenge that which needs to be challenged. You urge us to see that nothing is just clean or dirty, black or white and everything that needs to be said can find its voice in your words, in your voice, and in your pen. Your words, both written and spoken have the S'Maatin twang, the Saba song, the Caribbeanness and the whole worldness in them. You represent the fact that as an artist and a goddess woman Saba has limitless hills and valleys that go hard beyond 5 square miles. You make the 37 square miles of Sweet S'Maatin reach 37000 square miles. Your words prove that there are no borders and walls that the artist cannot overcome and that the fullness of what you say and write connects to the fullness of our collective lived experiences from wherever we come from. We can all hear the stories and see ourselves somehow in your work.

Lysanne, your words are a constant inspiration, your writings the etching of a painting, full of color, a constant discovery and rediscovery. The melodies you evoke; the colors, the rhythms, the textures, the taste, the moves, the whynes, the groans, the moans, the questions, the answers, all manage to explode off pages when necessary or float and dance in the air when needed or envelop when they want to or challenge when they have to. I am grateful for your constant, consistent work, through the thick, the thin, the good, the bad, the ugly, the love, the anger, the hurting, the hate, the sexy, the fullness, the fcukness, everything. I am grateful that the words keep coming, that you keep writing, that you allow the words to be written through you and that you continue to share them with us. We are better for having them to guide us towards the reminders that there are always more than just what the eyes see; there is what the ears hear, what the intuition senses and what the heart knows.

Clara Reyes
Artist & Ally
St. Maarten, October, 2018

introduction

In the beginning, there was not Eve, but Lilith. Lilith, however, was written out of history because she refused to acknowledge the inequality of women. She jumped the wall around the garden of Eden and chose to leave Adam's domination to become her own woman: assertive, courageous, and independent.

In *HER(E), A Collection of Queer Caribbean LGBTI Affirming Poems and Short Stories*, the reader will find a reflection of this indomitable spirit as well as a homage to women loving women. The poems consist of four parts: warrior, lov(h)er, sweetjuice, and rainbow. The two short stories that follow are: 'creation in rewrite' and 'daughters.' Both poems and stories make use of an alternative spelling of words that are embedded in our minds as being written in stone. – Is god masculine or feminine, or neutral? If god is a woman is she named a god/is, or a god/dess? – The author has a playful attitude to language and inserts 'nation language' of various Caribbean countries into her texts, as well as colloquial words borrowed from feminism and/or Rastafari. She effortlessly mixes rhyme and rhythm and some of the poems are best read aloud.

Standing on the shoulders of Lilith, Sappho, Audre, Anahita, and all the great-great-great grandmothers before her, Lysanne Charles takes us into the colorful world of LBGTI. A world inhabited by warriors and lovers, goddesses and strong women who seemingly

got lost in history. When a group of persons are omitted from the canon of history, each generation will have to discover anew those who came before. And that is exactly what Charles does. She wants to know: "Who were our queer ancestors?" And when she finds out she wants to speak out, for she is a warrior and "*silence is not an option*," nor is "*the contempt of society*." But the warrior is also a 'lov(her)' as becomes clear in the first three parts of the poems. Love can be sweet and sumptuous, getting drunk on every part of your lover's body, as in 'sweet juice'. However, love does not always come easy, nor is it without peril:

> *I am used to crossfire now*
> *more prepared*
> *but my chest is still not bullet proof*
> *god/dess still reaches her mark*
> *stray bullets still reach my heart*
>
> [stray bullet, p. 30]

Love can also come in many roles, as wife/sister/mother/daughter/queen/friend ... or even father/brother, for: "... *in some lives we switch sex and gender...*" [lives, p. 33]

The poems in the first three parts seem mainly nurtured by personal experiences of love – its joy and anguish. Yet in the last part the author speaks with a voice that goes beyond the personal and becomes political in a plea for a new world:

we came to understand that diversity
could not be a catch phrase
if we were to construct new ways
so that we did not waste
one single soul
that our goal(s) had to be
bigger than the ones we were told
or the ones we were sold

or the ones passed down to us
in an empty inheritance
[in the year of our Lorde, p. 70]

Lysanne Charles has created a collection of poetry that speaks about a struggle for freedom and equality for the LBGTI community, as well as for its happiness and integration. For readers who prefer prose to poetry, the two short stories will allow them to get a glimpse of the mindscape of the author.

In her story 'creation in rewrite' Charles refashions old mythic conventions and creates her own. "*Womyn*" is no longer fashioned from a man's rib, nor is she created "male and female in the image of God". According to the gospel of the Goddess Eye Charles, in the beginning only females were created. However, after witnessing the multiplication of the animals they requested for "*those that were not like them*" to be able to procreate as well.

'daughters' deals with a lesser known group added to the LGBT tribe, the I or intersex person. Born with sex

characteristics that aren't entirely male or female a person could decide to live as a man or a woman or alternate between the two like Virginia Woolfe's Orlando. In 'daughters' Charles subtlety introduces the issue in the desperate desire of a man who tries to have a son, but only begets daughters. Ironically his wish is finally fulfilled after his death when his last child, born "*neither boy nor girl, or maybe both … registered as male in the island's registry*".

Lysanne Goddess Eye Charles did not have to jump the wall like Lilith to speak her mind and live the life she wants to live. Like her sister/mentor Audre Lorde she has learned to accept diversity and celebrate it. May we all learn to do the same.

Maria van Enckevort – Cijntje
Curaçao, October 2018

HER(E)

poems

warrior

1. women like me

in some places/women still die/for being women like me/so I cannot let my silence save me /what is my society's contempt/compared to their society's' knives~bullets~ropes and other instruments of torture/and all because we love her/(always,sometimes,mainly,only) her/because we're lov(h)ers/because we love our chests rounded/hips flared/because some lips are (naturally) softer than others/and we prefer(r)e(d) them/because loving her feels so right/these women pay for their ability to extract rhythms even from fear/for transgressions deemed deviant to them who will not understand nor hear/they pay for their unwillingness to dance in closets/when club lights are calling/and staying underground only forces them away from the rainbows they be/they pay/with blood/membrane/mutilations/even death/and still they come/out/ in villages, towns, cities/families, schools, jobs/governments, societies, histories/~memories~/they are still coming/still/feeling, fighting, forcing

HER(E)

FREEDOM/because the alternative is like dying too/and it dishonors them/who go/no longer slaves/those who are the brave/to deaths/often times horrendous/while we keep coming/ still/out/in/over/our whispers becoming roars/can you hear us/we are Sappho's
daughters/and/we/love/…women/and because I love women/I cannot be silent/it will not save me

2. saturday

this saturday feels like i[1] do/grey/with bits of
color peeking through/and all the colors are
you/rainbow ranger/warrior friend/who
worried about my heart/and traveled through
cyberia/under roughest seas/and windy
airwaves/to reach to me/and eye can only tell
you this/that it was one moment/of
intense~est pain/the extinguishing of a
flame/but it was just that/an hour, a minute, a
second/a moment/and it could last
only as long
as I allowed it to...

[1] I make use of the terms Eye, I & i throughout this book. It is influenced by the I&I used in the Rastafarian philosophy which is an expression utilized to encompass the idea of oneness. In this case, the writer uses Eye, I and i to reference the totality of her being, with Eye representing her highest self or goddess energy, I representing her human self, fraught with all the complex experiences and energies that come along with that and i representing her lower human self. This concept also falls in line with the zodiac sign Scorpio, under which the I fall, which speaks of the scorpion having three manifestations, the phoenix, the eagle and the scorpion itself. Finally, it references the idea of a trinity as often found in many western religions.

3. tight ropes

we all walk tightest ropes/between
annihilations and redemptions/negotiate
treaties for peaces/or for piece/dual with
darkness for de-light/or lighterness for
depth/carry ourselves out into nights to
outrun demons/outrum phantoms/outwine
regrets/bury ourselves beneath bodies/in
attempts to cleave ourselves whole/as if that
be our sole purpose/and if we grow/we
glow/ever brighter/and if we stumble/we
falter/alter... ourselves for altars not our
own/commit real sacrilege/carnage of
souls/in order to meet society's standards/in
order to achieve someone else's goals/and
those who bend norms/who will not
conform/we slaughter them for their
bravery/because they prefer death to
slavery/because they prefer fallings to
nests/dare to venture out sooner rather than
cling to breasts/lest the breasts belong to
someone other/than a mother/these be the
freaks that outfreak freud/outqueer the
noise/create themselves from voids/sort of
like android god-desse-s/essentially we

humans/*wom(b)ans*[2]*/who dare to claim ourselves as lovers/cite lilith as our mother/midmorning ramblings/samplings from rhythms set/*you ain seen nothing yet*/some may wish their flesh dead/but me eye'll kcuf my longings on their own heads/take myself to bed and come out spent/but eye won't repent/not for living/not for loving/not for longing/not for desire/nor the fire that makes me me/*eye'ma be...free.../I'ma be free.../i'ma be free…*

[2] Where italics are used it is to indicate that I am using some form of 'nation language' or colloquial English, whether it is Caribbean, American or otherwise belonging to a sub-culture. In this case, womban refers to an early feminist alternative to the word woman.

4. then let me be brave!

then let me be brave,
let me be no slave to customs and vague,
ancient ideologies
to peoples or what they may expect of me
let me rage
make my life my own stage
forge on unafraid
pay what there is to be paid
so when I go to my grave
I go free
unencumbered by what society
anticipated I'd be
instead I'd go me
110 percent glam/bull/dyke
if that's what I like
110 percent slam on this mic
you wanted a love poem, well *psyche*
this is a love poem for me
a hard poem for me
tired of trying to be
all for everybody
leaving nothing for me
driving me to my knees
always trying to please

making futile attempts to appease
and instead losing me
when I just want to breathe
breathe,
breathe,
please
let me ease my distress
that won't let me progress
that won't let me fly
keeps me grounded
afraid to try
come chase this dis-ease
that won't release me
come let me be brave
come let me be brave
come let me be brave
let me walk with the courage I crave
to shake myself free
of elements that try to suppress who I be
Eye be me
and it is enough
don't like it - tough
I'ma live my life
with a husband or a wife
and if the time comes alone
cause I am my own home

HER(E)

done got fully grown
i do not need approval
I need peace
piecing myself back whole
self-acceptance my goal
I want to be brave
i need to be brave
come let me be brave
come let me be brave
no longer a slave
no longer a slave
come let me be brave

5. straight out of eden

i want space to breathe/room to imagine me's of which i'd never before dreamed/does this piss you off/make you uncomfortable/mess with your norms/*kcuf* with your laws/of course/and still i'm that force/to be reckoned with/cause.../

i'm not one/but a legion/we're lilith's daughters/so we followed our mother straight out of eden/for that we've been called heathens/just cause we can't be believing/that our god/creates hu(e)mans/less perfect than yours/still you insist on waging wars/against us/can't resist building cages in attempts to fence us/but your tactics won't work trust us/cause/

we stand tall on sapphic shoulders who lived long before sappho/tried to remove us from your hi(s)stories/and still we won't go/we're countless generations of *womyn* who made lives together that communities didn't understand/we're that one mother, sister, great aunt who always walked like a man/we've always been there/and we always will/try to bend us/break us/end us/...and we keep coming… still...

 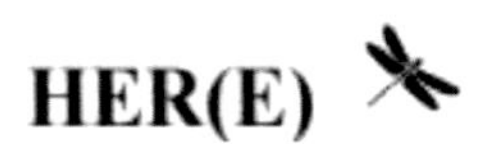

6. bun fyah

you want to bun fire on me/but be prepared for when eye burn fyah back/bun with seriousness for that *ish* that you chat/better yet get ready for when eye bring my fyah pack/rainbow warriors, but ain none of us weak/matter of fact we now reaching for your peaks/we don't need no turn the other cheeks/gots my own moral compass/so to hell with yours/you so busy in my business/ain keeping scores with yours/*son*/i'm not confused/i'm just confusing you/so you want to tell me how to think about the very things that i can do/you want to relegate me to the fringes of my own story/can't see the common enemy so you want to 'other' me/you want to order my reality/well none of my eyes will buy your fantasies/won't get caught up on your (ph)fall(i)a{c}ies/your truths can never contain or define me/i'm doing fine *b*/so go bring your fire/trust i'mma bring mine/in fact/everyday eye light new fyahs to burn in my mind/some words flow/some words rhyme/but believe me i'm listening, learning, growing, claiming me all the time/so bun fire upon me/it only drives me to dig farther/bun fire on me/it only makes me think

further/come bun fire on me/the resistance
makes me wiser/oh please come bun your
fire/distract yourself from our dilemmas/yes,
come bun fire pon me/that is my
desire…fyah...fyah…pure fyah

7. sinatra, i do it my way

true to my rainbow colored wings/eye want to fly/bust out of my cocoon/and cause ripples that will become waves from the vibrations of my movements/let my beating cause echoes/that reverberate across realities/yours and mine/my voice wants to create more than sound/it wants to reshape meaning/I'm *feining**/for an opportunity/to be me/to be free…

so i want my tombstone to read/she was a fan of sinatra/there wasn't a rule around/that she didn't doctor/age didn't tame her/it only made her hotter/the game that tried to claim her/was no match for lilith's daughter/a coors[3] in one hand/sometimes a kools[4] in the next/who wanna vex vex/who wanna text text/all who wanna step/just gotta come proper/give it your all/or your next best offer...lol...

don't polish up my image/i like it tarnished/covered me up in so much

---

[3] References a type of beer that was popular on the island of Sint Maarten.

[4] References a brand of cigarette.

stories/it's like i'm varnished/glossed over truths/for many surface is better than roots/so you stay at superficial/while i'll never be artificial/so many tales of my exploits it's like i'm a legend/or rather they be making me legendary/rumor has it i've had so many bitches[5] on my tongue is scary/or maybe i should be scared see/cause the way they paint it i stay horny/or just give horns easy/fuck any random cheesy/just to please me/in ya'll tales i stay bad/so i'm not going to defend that/i live hard and maybe fast/but at least i'm living and not half-assed/you color me grimey/i rebuke it/my rhymes speak/stop sweating my swag *g**/and let who loves me love me/you all up in my business/just don't get it twisted/you'll never scope the truth/damn you blinked and missed it/but don't trip/just mind your own matters/eye am my own master/leaning on universal energies and the strength of my ancestors/so I will not let your bullshit settle or fester/i don't want your pedestals or thrones/i'm

[5] Author dislikes the use of the word bitch in reference to women, but wrote this piece in the manner in which the rumors came to her.

HER(E)

creating my own/your standards mean
nothing to me/built brick upon brick on pure
*bull-ish** and hypocrisy/even the devil has a
devil/i call her god/so best act like you know
and *kcuf* what you heard...

HER(E)

lov(h)er

1. fragments of you

what is the consequence of joy/

sorrow/

and so i want to borrow old words and break them/shake them up/recreate them/make them into something new/something true/so that i can begin to explain again the presence of absence/the ever absent presence of you/there is a lesson in balance to be learnt here/the price of imbalance the extreme fear...of falling/like I fell and shattered/soul scattered by the whims of madness/i reeled on my axis...but still could not grasp it/and so came to understand that all voids echo/especially the ones which cannot be let go/create spaces where memories reverberate/and amplify/mnemosyne rebirths wisps and twists of your reflections/and they

HER(E)

resonate in places where i cannot fake
amnesia/though sometimes my heart wishes it
could be administered anaesthesia/because
eye cannot forget moons which once shown
brightest bright/after darkest night(s)/and
lighted the way back to a semblance of
being/loving you was freeing/however
fleeting/and now even silences are familiar
with my screams/i dream of you both
often/still it doesn't soften/the sorrow of the
void your leaving left
behind/sometimes...hints of you
remain/phantom energies/spectres of de-
light/and i remember it being you and
eye/that is the weight of
memories/buoyant/but burdensome/aether-
like/holding together a me that sometimes
feels as if it is close to bursting apart/except i
am honoured to still carry you in my heart/so

HER(E)

my word

is...bittersweet/bitterssweet/i...retreat

somewhere within myself to a moment when

I was more wise...because of you/you re-

taught me about the beauty of sacrifice/and

the exquisiteness of that recollection must

suffice/in the absence of your presence/i

cannot bring myself to speak of you in past

tense/my heart takes offense/at any attempts

to delete you/even though i know i must let

you go/for all of your energies to synergize

and grow/but sometimes...i just want to see

you-hear you –hold you/and then remember

you are no longer the kiddies i recall in my

mind/i have not learnt the skill of harnessing

and bending time/and you bloom

on/blossoming in the rays of your suns'

gaze/and i am left with bitterssweet/in search

of ma'at/in search of my art/in search of

meaning/gently weaning myself from
memories/so that you can be free/and i can
be one half of two goddesses co-creating
stability/the ability to ride the tides/and arrive
back to selves/having delved beneath the
superficial truths/and i am better for having
known you/offspring enigmas/there is no
longer the need to figure out the past/it could
not last/and yet it happened/once upon a
brilliant instant/in a flash of chaos which
burnt until blister/you were my soul's charges
too/and now, forever, i carry ...fragments of
you.....

2. wings

eye offer you wings/you want to cling to cages/

i want to bust up paradigms/

you love the wisdoms of the ages/

norms don't fit me/

you wonder why i challenge normativity/

eye want to explain to you how it suppresses my creativity/

but lately/

i've sensed that words aren't enough/

sometimes even crossings over we want to make are tough/

again...again...again...eye find myself here/

laying a heart open/

making myself bare/

attraversiamo... can we cross over...even this/

a philosophical divide/both deep and wide/

something's amiss/

chasms calling for mental adjustments/

HER(E)

shifts in points of view/

you trying to get me/me trying to get you/

eye cannot force my truth on yours/

it would only become your lie/

you cannot force your truths on me/

within them eye-I-i would die/

overly dramatic/i can be that/

but eye'm always open to reasonings/

application of communication to both of our pleasings/

life is too short to get buried in the mix-ups/

let's continue to explore theories and keep these just minor hiccups/

eye don't work with first or last places/

eye just want to work in and from spaces of abundance/

eye'm being redundant/

arguing my case again/

attraversiamo/come let us cross over and transcend

3. a guarded heart

eye do not want to love from behind a
guarded heart/

but eye will/if i have to/erect walls to protect
a spirit battered/

a soul adrift/will pluck-painfully-rose colored
scales from my eyes/

peel away illusions until I no longer see in
abstracts/

no longer make allowances for flaws which
border on disrespect/they may foster
disrespect/fester like disrespect

eye will have you know/that loving me is an
honor/a privilege/

to be loved by me is sacrosanct/a ceremony
of my soul/an opening of my heart to
worship all of you/not the parts deemed

HER(E)

acceptable or worthy/but their opposites and
all the in betweens/

eye would have you know/

I am slow to love/and even slower to let
go/...but if eye must/I will love with less
trust/less unconditionally/eye will save
myself/lest I lose all of me...

4. same bird

same birds sing same songs
i remember
waking… waking… waking up
to a letter propped on the pillow where you had slept
begging me to forget her and come love you
not to be afraid of your love
it would not fit tight like a glove
but would sit loose enough to keep me choosing you
as if it was a choice and not a calling

a love allowing me to continue seeking what was real and true within myself
were i to know then
-- in that blacked out room above
what i now know
-- on this sidewalk down below
-- that all love is destined for some sorts of disappointments
some sooner than others
and that even though when we became lovers
crashing into each other under covers
where each bedding meant the birthing of

something we called love
we too would cave to the pressures we faced
and desert our center for sides
where night and heartache would ride us into
the edges
where we would hide for peace
from this thing we called love
until we ceased
deceased to be born again
into the arms and hearts of new women

same birds sing same songs
and i remember waking… waking… waking
up
to new birds singing new songs
and a text from her
-- begging me to let go of the past
and choose what's next
a new her, begging me,
anew,
to now forget you….

5. stray bullet

she struck me
like a stray bullet
and i
caught in heavy crossfire
was unprepared
i had no bulletproof chest
so she poured in
and words fell me
i fell in love
in/cense burned
and curtains parted
she took me in
and under/covers
i sought refuge
in her warmth
in finger play
and rhythmic incantations
in the stretch of limbs
across amber sheets
her words like waters
called for immersion
and i wanted to dip myself 3x/s
rename myself hers
and come out whole
but in my con/fusion
eyes could not see her
so i could not treat her

HER(E)

like the god/dess she was
like the god/dess she's being
i drank from her rivers
but could not taste her
so silence
took the place of sounds
of sighs
and there was this uneasy dis/connection
no language to bridge the divide
i drifted further from god
what good is god if she does not heal
god could not reach me
so eye could not reach her
fell pitifully into failure
words could not save us
left us refugees in love
clinging desperately to a life raft
that was already sinking
submerged in desolation
i could not get beyond the words
heard only in my head
echoing perpetually between ego and pride
i saw no salvation
for her or i
i took the first train and rode out
but could not
cannot stop my neck from turning
looking back for…her

HER(E)

i am used to crossfire now
more prepared
but my chest is still not bullet proof
god/dess still reaches her mark
stray bullets still reach my heart

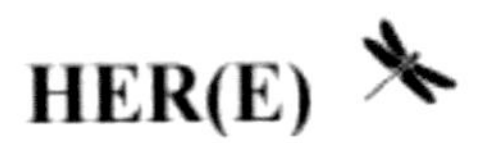

6. lives

she's my wife
in another life
where we wake up to
koffie verkeerd mocca tainted kisses
breakfast quickies on countertops
where she makes my breath stop
mixing sacred ancient scents
with the smells of burnt eggs
stove top heat raise legs
and we beg each other for release
but do not cease
bald hazel head
embracing gray-speckled tar curls
she holds hips which would rather twirl
hot breaths cross fiery lips
while tongues meet
greet the morning
in a ritual of passion
in a spiritualness that we fashion

the goddesses awakens
to soft cries
beautiful head nestled between warm thighs
hands find breasts

while others anchor and knees bend upward
pushed by arched feet
spirits meet
take flight
and neon colors mingle
in rainbow delights
moans reach out to touch sighs
and we achieve heights
which defy boundaries and conventions
our bodies bask in each other's attentions
our movements shakes us
take us to climaxes beyond one realm
dimensions
and in other lives we feel this bond
lived where we are wives
beyond what we have here and there and
there and there
for we live that life in a singular realm
in another world
where we are more than just best girls
in another place and time
where she claims me as hers and i claim her as
mine

see she's my sister
on a different plain

vertical lives lived ensure that all that remains
are continued energies linking her to me
always, forever, constantly, perpetually
we're infinity
in yet another life i call her daughter
and in yet another she's my mother
in some lives we switch sex and gender
so sometimes she's my father or i'm her
brother
catching glimpses through dreams
when there are breaks in the seams
of boundaries separating time
back to lives lived when she is mine
where we live deep in each other rhythms
hard on each other's rhymes
where we wake up daughter and son
named for the goddess and god they are
tickle them with mommy kisses
remind them they are stars
that the universe is their playground
that no worries can confound or confuse
them
that they have nothing to lose then
not even themselves
cause they've got mommies behind them
where lives together have just begun

where we relish in the cocoon we've spun
together
riding tight in any weather
where she's my wife
in another life

in this life she's my powerful soul sista friend
ours is a cycled circle that sees no end
clichés cannot do justice to what we be
these words can only just begin to touch it
souls entwined, hearts in rhythm
more than having backs, we have missions
propelling each other past crippling
insecurities
promising each other we'll be fine when we
reach our full maturities
she's my ankhher
anchoring me to reality and still reminding me
of dreams
she's more than my queen
she's part of me from pasts/futures when we
were one being

so though in this lifetime we wake up to other
wives
we recognize we're still bonded through all

realms and lives
she makes sure i won't break, though i may bend
i make sure she remembers she is perfect,
something she can't quite comprehend
*we go good together**, a complex blend
we've known each other before, we'll know each other again
she's my wife in another life
but in this life i'm honored to call her my friend

 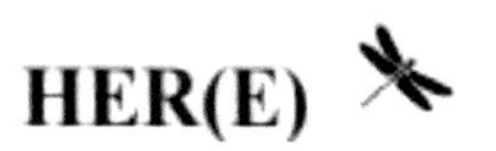

7. falling

this is why i hate falling/bruises hurt/even the heart/and some wounds take longer to heal than others/leave keloids on surfaces/once smooth/broken bones cannot compare to this/there is medication/for such mending/~but this~/who understands the need to curl up/position fetal/sleep/the inhalation of numb-ers/lethal/attempts to find solace at the bottom of the cup/drowning in liquids- amber/this longing to not remember this is why eye fear god/not because she's vengeful/but because she's vain/oops...pain/the price to pay for worship/too high/sometimes/the cost of homage/disillusion/confusion/chaos/soul adrift/but experience knows knowledge/brings wisdom/there is no need to lose ankhher/in order to find her/paradox

of love/lose yourself/forfeit god/forfeit
god/lose yourself/somewhere there is
balance/waiting to be
found/somewhere/somewhere/not here...

love...is not a game/but it is a science/first
application...self-reliance/second rule...know
the laws/all that causes suffering is placed on
pause/because/there can be no higher cause...
than self-acceptance/practice presence/know
your own essence/this is essential/love is
elemental/embracing your own goddess be
fundamental/pedestal-ing other's deity is
detrimental/to your well-being/own your be-
ing/that is the most freeing aspect of
love/own it/throne it/know it....that is the
science of love....

8. chokehold

you loved me with the desperation of a chokehold

left me gasping for air thoughts unclear energies sapped heart bruised but beating,...unbeaten it took me forever to recover

though, the steadiness of my limbs came back too slowly see your energies had muddied my being had left me seeing...double sometimes even in threes left me seeing me and you, you and me and...you but never, ever...me... i forgot who i was and who i was to become undone buried under the forced transplant of you my body became a tomb for me, making room for you to conquer my heart and mind leaving most of me behind until i could barely find the markers guiding me back to my soul your goals had become my goals your dreams morphed into my dreams somewhere in the dim recesses of my memories she screamed...and waited for the glass to fall and shatter scatter your focus so that you could release your grip refocus mine so that i could

slip free finally back to me gasping, grasping
at the remnants of me stumbling to my feet
heart beaten but still beating and your love,
desperate, distanced finally so i can breathe

9. poem-in-parts & pieces

1.

i chose to fall
knowing that this goddess
would not catch me
and she did not
and now i remember
that this is what sorrow feels like
this a/salt/ing of cheeks
water breaking its banks
sudden compressions of heart
gasping of breath
this abrupt death
--sort of
how do i start to explain this sadness
there is no abstract way
to write about this falling heart first
--into (this) god
with a persistent thirst for more
but--
why has she forsaken me
shaken me up and out of my slumber
s/c/ent me to du/a/el with the demons
of longing and loneliness
eye was (finally) fine
and now--

again eye know that
re/covering from love
can be a slow sweet passing
and so i die again

2.

can eye hide myself in you
from memories of her
would you mind
being mine
just for this minute
please help me forget
or better yet
remember
--a time before her
and recall that eye existed still
come kill this pain
that marches through my heart
in no particular rhythm
that numbs my spine
and stills my mind
until i am wordless
i used to pen odes to her
sing sacred hymns
cast blessings out
to kiss her cheeks
and send grace to whisper in her ear

eye(s) see god in you
there was no altar
more revered than hers
but--
may i borrow yours
scatter flowers
burn candles and incense
wrap myself in/scents
--not hers
draw new waters
for worship

3.

anahita[6] speaks to me
says go no deeper
the waters are tricky
--here--
though they are a salty sweet
they are
wont to change at moment's notice
so
i send up red flares for rescue
and they brave the currents
swim out and meet me
these waters have become too crafty

---

[6] Anahita is an Indo-Iranian Goddess associated with water, fertility, healing and wisdom.

to traverse alone
on my own
i'm drowning
cramping all over
weighted down by chimeras
of my own making
no more real
than nightmares
daydreams can cause sorrow too
they come to meet me
the wise ones
assembled wisdom
become buoy-ers of life
more than lift me up
they lead me in
there is mercy in some groundings

4.

sometimes
the promise is not enough
especially when only eye(s)
can see the potentials
sometimes even when god/is there
she cannot be felt
so i know what lonely feels like
like some memories which bring demons
where once was de/light

i was your sacrifice
hurled with all your rage
against your cage
and still
--could not break it
            --cannot break it
what is the rite thing
--or wrong thing--
to say
when all i want to say is
eye(s) worship you
--i see you still
it is not enough
to pierce
fortresses of your own construction
and eye am afraid of heights
so i dare not scale them
--which leaves us
to destructions all our own

5.

eye must convene the council of wise one
let her remind me
that i am better than this
that i know better than this
and even though eye will miss your kiss
i will survive

and if eye(s) stay open
i will even thrive
eye am alive
breathing still
what doesn't fatten
may kill
but what is death
compared to this
this rending apart of chest plate
to reveal a traumatized heart
atrophied lungs
no longer capable of breathing
eye(s) knew
--indeed--
where this was leading
and still i chose this falling

6.

i should know by now
how to fall into god
without crashing
keyed in as eye am
to the wisdom
that no/thing is everlasting
but this does not stop the pain
of being amongst the fallen
--again--

for having found god
and then lost her
and becoming a seek(h)er
--once more--
and now eye know this
that the only thing
truer than seeing god in you
is knowing that she resides in me
this is a freedom
which is not fleeting
so eye am no atheist
count me still amongst the believers
those who know that it is possible
to live wide open
travel to form-iliar shores
fall into depths unfathomable
and return
without regrets
to love

10. closure

1.

sometimes closure's not about conversations/but about closing doors/serving notice: your heart doesn't live here anymore/for sure/it use to claim ownership of my breathing/had me believing/that without you my breath would start seizing/stalling/that i would be falling/falling apart...

2.

every time you came for me/but didn't stay/i was forced to find new ways of loving you/take refuge in my own understanding/remain undemanding/keep standing/even when i felt like laying love down/me staying down/giving up/giving you up/calling it quits/but that was no way to live/still i lived it...for you...

3.

what was the shelf life on our love/i wish i'd known it in advance/the expiration date of our romance/the production date of

madness/in my boldness-badness/i might have stopped the manufacturing of anger and hate/and saved us the grief/before it was too late/found different ways for letting go of a love so brief/found other ways to relief...to release...

4.

i used to search walls for fragments of you/of us/looking in disgust/for who we used to be...i wanted to remember/i wanted to forget/since there was no going back/no turning back time/i scrolled back/until i found a place where you used to be mine/i used to wish you would have had the faith/to make the break/to take those first real steps in my direction/had the courage to do more than tentative stutterings/though eye know even those took courage too/but how naive i was upon reflection/for having ever believed in....you...

5.

once i thought your winks were mine/but i know now i was playing blind/blinded by the illusion/of a vision i so desperately

needed/for healing/i was fiening* for breath/and you brought me fresh air/when i would have gladly chosen death/or rather thought i was dying/i would be lying if i said/i do not recall/at all...

6.

now i suffer from phantom lov(h)ers syndrome/ironic that its abbreviation is pls/as in please/as in bitch please/or maybe goddess please get yourself together/as if the universe is screaming goddess get real/remember your being/this (r)evolution...

7.

because eye know like continents we may be pulled apart by forces greater than ourselves

8.

i use to think i longed for the lov(h)ers lost/but wondered what it was i really missed/a look-a touch-a word-a kiss/the dream of people they used to be/the dream of what was us/was me.../lov(h)ers got up and left their ghosts/i stayed behind to play host to parts/sometimes/i don't mind/i remain in

the realm of reason/sorting out the seasons
passed/the past lives in me/even when i wish
the past would let me be...

11. let go

i am not ready to let go
and yet I must
for freedom
to be free
I must release you
eye must let life flow
in the direction of growth to grow
and so
I go
and eye, I, i
release you

12. how to reclaim a heart

start at the edges and work your way towards
the center
pause when you must
pause if you must
realize when you cannot erase memories or
forget them ...
embrace them
and when they scream to cry, let them
and when they strain to die, let them
cradle them gently and usher them towards
the ether where they will return to energies to
become again....
remember not all moments are meant to be
remembered... forever...
remember that while balance is the aim you
cannot be centered forever....
so when you are finally at your center, bow
into yourself again....bow unto yourself again...
for you have made it back to your own altar
relish in your return to self...but do not
remain there...
do not falter
dwell only momentarily at this holiest of
sites... take respite
then dash again for the margins
there is no living in the light, without some

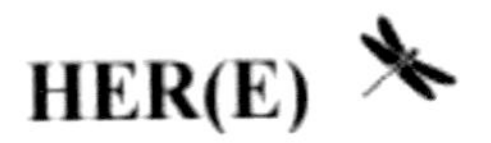

HER(E)

darkness
the periphery beckons, the whirlwind calls
you survived the fall to rise again

13. moonrising

may moonrising always bring a sense of peace
an urge to slow down a desire to cease seeking
may it signal a time for self
for selffullness
for silence
keeping
for moon baths when she is full
naked and wild if you dare
to bare your all before her who calls the tides
who knows that all that flows ebbs in time
may you be prone
in whatever season of yourself
maiden mother crone
to find your way back home
to the refuge that is self
may you bask in her silver wealth
and at moonset
let your eyes
ride the skies
and memories take flight
you were loved

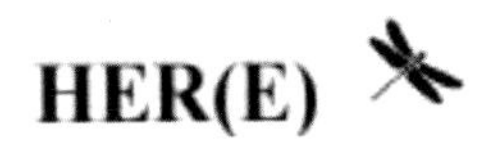

you are love
you are light

HER(E)

sweetjuice

1. i never knew

i never knew
i never knew
i never knew

i never knew you had nerves in your ears
i mean they're just your ears
until my lips kissed you there
and sent your spirit dancing
until my whispers hit you there and set your blood to boiling
i never knew-

i never knew you had nerves in your neck
i mean, come on, baby it's just your neck
until my breath brushed you there
and set your brain to humming
until my fingers sought you there
and set your stomach clenching
i never knew-

i never knew you had nerves in your armpits
they're armpits, baby, just armpits,
until i caressed you there
and set your body tingling
until i nuzzled there

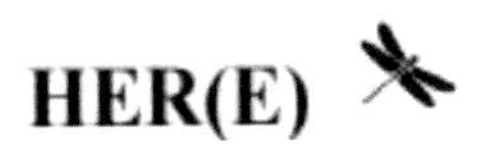

and set you ablaze with longing
i never knew-

i never knew you had so many nerves in your
breasts
your sweet breasts baby, i just never knew
until i kissed your nipples
and set your throat to moaning
until i sucked them sweetly
and set your lips to parting
i never knew-

i never knew you had nerves in your back
in the curves of your beautiful back,
until my mouth rained kisses there
and set your spine to arching
until my tongue made rivers there
and set your butt to swaying
i never knew-

i never knew you had nerves in your
bellybutton
your bellybutton, your bellybutton
until i nibbled you there
and set your thighs to trembling
until i licked you there
and set your skin to shivering
i never knew-

HER(E)

i never knew you had oh so many nerves in
your …*(smile)*
until i touched you there
until i kissed you there
until i sucked you there
and set your back to arching
and set your butt to lifting
and your … hmmmm…to weeping
honestly, baby, i honestly, just never knew.

 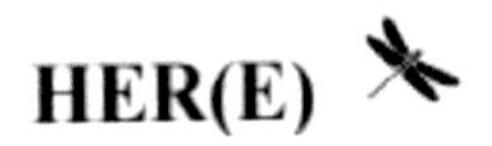

2. sugar apple

before you eat
i have to watch you... eat...
a sugar-apple
i have to see if your mouth knows form
how to form itself over flesh ... and suck
if your tongue knows how to duck and
bend itself in all directions
seeking sweetness
and then
once found
how to scoop it out
i have to see if your teeth
knows how to raze skin
while your tongue slurps circles
around tantalizingly tender portions of ....
sugar
i have to see what you do with chin juice
and moistured mustaches
what your nose does with scents so
intoxicating
you get drunk or high from proximity
see
i need to hear
if your throat moans in in anticipation of
ecstasy

and if it groans with the joy of fulfillment
to feel if your body relaxes as it climaxes
from satiation
then rises again as your strength courses with
renewed power
for such is the nature of my longing
to be split open
parted
and devoured and devoured
and devoured

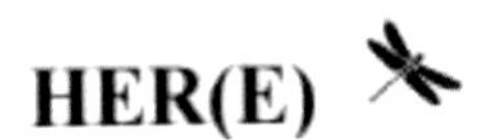

3. watch me move

like the jiggle in my breasts

watch me move

like the bounce in my butt

watch me move

like the sway of my hips

watch me move

i am a black woman

wonderful and mystique

men take one look

salivate and weep

like the quiver of my thighs

watch me move

like the brown-sugar that are my legs

watch me move

like the shape of my calves

watch me move

HER(E)

men take a glance

and want to go to bed

but take my word

ain't thoughts of sleep in they heads

like the curve of my smile

watch me move

like the slope of my nose

watch me move

like the glint in my eye

watch me move

they stop and look

when i'm walking down the street

cause i'm a dredded black goddess

beckoning for them to worship at my feet

like the taste of my lips

watch me move

like the feel of my tongue

watch me move

HER(E)

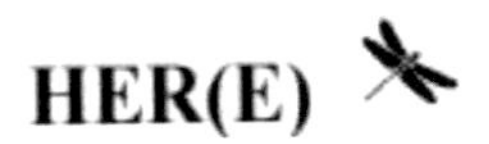

like the nip of my teeth

watch me move

cause i'm a lover of men

and a lover of women too

cause once you go this

without it you could never do

like the arch of my spine

watch me move

like the moan in my throat

watch me move

like that velvet that you feel

watch me move

cause i am woman

graceful but wild

so dare to come closer

look inside and be beguiled

rainbow

1. in the years of our Lorde[7]

in the years of our Lorde[8]
b/lessons be upon her, ashe [9]
we learned that **silence would not protect us**[10]
would not save us
so we should speak
se were taught to *tun up* patriarchy
so unearth old molds of be-ing and imagine new beings
re-image- in and of ourselves

in the years of our Lorde
blessing be upon her, ashe
the political became personal
and the personal became political
and we became women warriors

---

[7] Audre Lorde was a Caribbean-American feminist, womanist, and civil rights activist, writer and poet. Her work often dealt with challenging oppressions and speaking for those she felt were treated unjustly.
[8] Throughout the poem this is the only word which is not lower cased; this in deference to Lorde.
[9] Ashe is derived from the Yoruba àṣẹ which means and so it will be.
[10] Lorde is famous for saying "Your silence will not protect you." It is often used in feminist and human rights activism circles.

HER(E)

because we realized
that sometimes warfare was unavoidable
and cowardice was not an option
when sis-stars died
while sis-stars died

in the years of our Lorde
blessing be upon her, ashe
we came to understand that diversity
could not be a catch phrase
if we were to construct new ways
so that we did not waste
one single soul
that our goal(s) had to be
bigger than the ones we were told
or the ones we were sold
or the ones passed down to us
in an empty inheritance

in the years of our Lorde
blessings be upon her, ashe
we became cyborg – god=is
and were recreated
both feminine and masculine
neither feminine nor masculine
essential individuals

constructed beings
part of the whole

in the years of our Lorde, ashe
we knew that bravery was not the absence of fear
but the fear of absence from ourselves
from ourselves
and so we became ---
a-she
a/she
a=she

ashe

 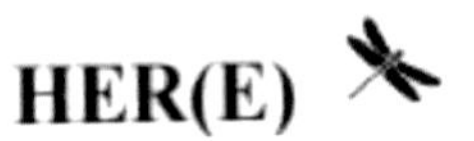

2. what the elders did not tell you

what the elders did not tell you
so you could not tell us
so we did not know
we now know and tell to those
who come behind us
though they seem to need no notice
they already know this
already live this...it appears
but just so we do not return to fear
let it be put out (t)here
stated clear...
that it is okay...
to be...free...
that who we be
has always been
we have always been
again...
and again...
and again...
from time's beginnings
but for centuries now they've tried to keep us
hidden
reworked our truth
twisted it in ways we found hard to refute
and rendered us mute and obscure

told us we were diseased
sent us scurrying for a cure
even though we were often sure...
that no treatment was needed
had we, in numbers, heeded
that intuition
would we have stood stronger against
admonitions
of societies who wished to closet us and
succeeded
until even we began to believe it
...that who we be
was unnatural
and so hid ourselves
and their truths about us
spoken long enough and loud enough became
factual
and so we came to fear ourselves
hate ourselves
and only those brave enough delve beyond
the bullshit
could reclaim it
it being...the chronicles of us
rainbow colored brilliant beneath the lies and
dust
do you remember so and so's sister who loved

HER(E)

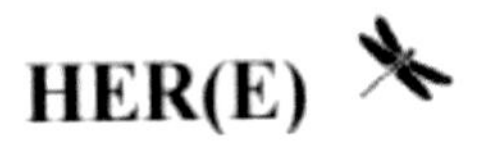

so and so's mother
they went good together[11]
or so and so's aunt who was the beloved so
and so' aunty
that is our history...also
because who we are
has always been
the rainbowed descendants
of rainbowed ancestors
sometimes birthing, always claiming
rainbowed offspring
there is no thing unnatural about us
except how you think
and what you thought
but should think no more
because who we are
we have been before
and will be forever more
despite the threat of death
despite the scorn
we were born into a tribe
queered
misunderstood and so feared
but we have no agenda save one

---

[11] This phrase was used on the Dutch Caribbean island of Saba in the olden days to reference women who love women.

to rebuke the lies which have been spun
and live the lives we've imagined
to tell our own stories with passion
in order to refashion
what the elders did not tell you…

3. eye want to tell you

eye want to tell you
eye want to tell you that you should not be
afraid of rainbows
that they are symbols of both beauty and
grace
that they carry covenants of sustenance if you
dare to follow them
and at the end there are pots of gold enough
to pave your own precious streets

eye want to tell you
eye want to tell you that you should not be
scared of rainbows
that they are sacred even unto us
that the fires of hell cannot burn as intensely
as the disgust you harbor for yourself because
you do not trust that you are imperfectly
perfect just the way you are

eye want to tell you
eye want to tell you
that somewhere in the center of rainbows
there is god
glorious as you've ever known god to be

reminding you that things do get better
that your ideas of yourself do get clearer
that that inner voice that you've been
programmed to hear does get dimmer
if you decide to redefine for yourself what is
sin, sinning or sinner
if you figure that you are worth weathering
storms to reach
that we are each god-loved in our own right

eye want to tell you
eye want to tell you that rainbows are not
scary
that they carry with them the promise of
rebirth, redemption, resolve and revolution
extraction from the delusion that something is
wrong with you
the confusion that who you are is caused by
nature gone askew
that you are an aberration, abnormal,
unnatural when all that is factual points out
another truth
that you..are..most simply you
rainbowed proud, beautiful, growing you
one-of-a-kind, radiant you

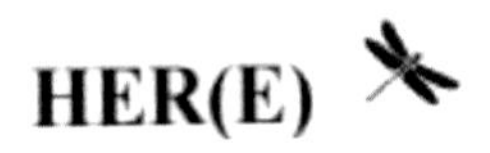

eye want to tell you
eye want to tell you that rainbows are ours
that there is so much more to this world than
what you know
and that if you are open and willing to grow
then rainbows can be bridges too
taking you over abysses that you think will
destroy you
over chasms you think would consume you
but if you are brave enough to brave them
and go
then you will blow your mind with brilliance
because you will have learned to be resilient
and rely mainly, chiefly, principally on yourself

eye want to tell you
eye want to tell you
eye want to tell you

4. **life**

to graduate life with honors and no regrets
to round the corner and charge down the stretch
to exit with the same optimism with which you enter
to survive both triumph and defeat and remain centered
to laugh in the face of sorrow but also shed a few tears
to love despite knowing the cost of loving is dear
to cling to those you love yet be able to let them go
and find solace from good-byes in the anticipation of hello

to long for each tomorrow and yet live for each today
to relish every moment whether at work or at play
to stay the course despite the many obstacles in your path
to do the right things out of love, not fear of wrath

to see the least amongst us and still find our
commonness
to look past lack of financial wealth and see
that you are blessed
to treat each man as an equal despite
superficial differences
to see the worst in others and still make
allowances
for the things that make us all alike and the
things that drive us all
and understand that everyone has moments in
which they appear to fall

to let your fear cause you to hesitate but not
allow you to not succeed
to let your ambitions drive you and yet not
succumb to greed
to embrace your weaknesses and then make
them your strengths
to live your life with courage no matter what
the expense
to stand for something you believe in
choosing to run against the herd
to understand that there aren't many things
more important that your word
to lose a few battles but eventually win the

war despite the cost
and understand to embrace the lessons from both victory and loss

to live with a true sense of passion despite what pain that brings
and doing so take pleasure from even the smallest things
to leave your life open to being touched by those who happen along your way
to be so moved by the earth's beauty that you have to pause and pray
to walk this earth with a keen sense of purpose to have accomplished all you would
all these are the things i wish for you and I'd grant you if eye could

 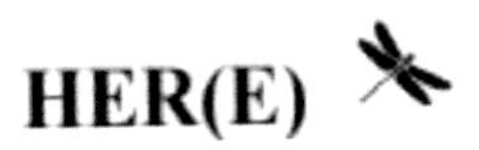

5. blurred lines/boundaries broken

in the space between gender bending
and gender breaking
is the place where she's awakening
sometimes she's clad in hanes for her
and other times hanes for him
her heels and wedges compete
for closet space
with her airforces and *tims*[12]
she can rock a skirt one day
and the next day she'll rock *dickies*[13]
some days she check the fellas and
other days she checks the chickies
she's not fake
will not conform to
paradigms and agreements
she did not make
it's her life at stake

mild tongues call her
non-conformist, troublemaker, rebel

---

[12] Short for Timberland, referencing a particular kind of boot the company is known for amongst American urban youth.
[13] Refers to the Williamson-Dickie Manufacturing Company, or Dickies which makes various types of work and school clothes. For youngsters on St. Maarten this brand was and remains popular for school and work uniforms.

HER(E)

those with sharper edges
label her dyke, lez, nasty and devil
but she walks on as she pleases
her *swaggas* not about fashion statements
so there's no one she appeases
she can pimp a full length dress
and/or even a three piece suit
every day with each decision
she lives her truth

no labels can box her in
mere words and phrases cannot define her
any thoughts of spiritual compromise
she's placed those far behind her
religious constraints try to oppress her
but the u/n/i/verse continues to bless her
she's a wave maker, risk taker
the world cannot break her
she may buckle
she may bend
but she'll never shatter again
she forges on
finally, concerned only
with her own reality
she knows her rainbow visions
and rhythms come naturally

but it wasn't always so…

HER(E)

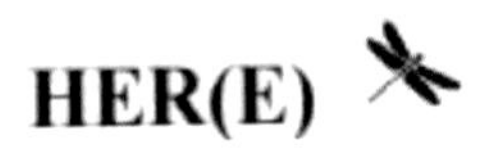

see at one point the world
tried to tame her
couldn't understand her *flex*
and tried to shame her
didn't comprehend the abstracts on her
canvas
so tried to frame her
labeled her *'other'*[14] and
tried to change her
but she fought back and found her way
so who can blame her
for being larger than life bigger than right
completely complex, complicated, convoluted
she's still de/light
her essence looms bright

gender bending
gender breaking
norms and rules are
hers for shaking
she charges ahead leaving
timid souls quaking
finally she's awakening

---

[14] Othering is the process of casting a group, an individual or an object into the role of the 'other' and establishing one's own identity through opposition to and, frequently, vilification of this Other.

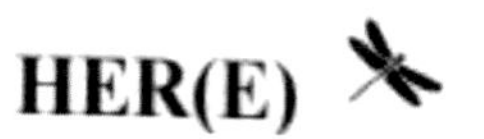

HER(E)

there is no male or female in her
there is only spirit
only infinite soul
and you better believe
following her own rhyme
right on her own time
stays her only goal!

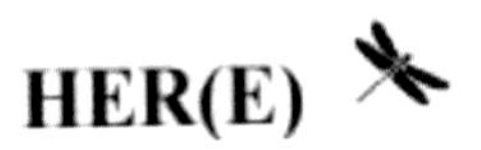

6. rainbow warriors

there is something to be said for being in the company of other warriors of the rainbow persuasion | those who own transgression | bend norms to their molding | she makes me consider all of my masculinities | allows me to appreciate her posterior and wonder | would i enjoy putting €•€£ on her | knowing her breast are padded onto chest | knowing her ample butt disguises the rest | that in normative society would make her a him | where chances of us getting together are slimmer than slim | but still here under neon, disco ball lights | she wants to be my delight | and why shouldn't I let her | what should I fear | that someone, somewhere will think that eye am a freak | will assault me and think I will turn the other cheek | that's not me | i'm a rainbow daughter | ready to throw water | break normativity | screw conformity | challenge expectations | mold my own relations(hip)s | shit! | eye'm ready to buss down beliefs | shake up prejudice(s) | eye just want to do this | eye just want to do this | eye just want to live...

7. man/girl

on your arm
walking the streets
of a city that never sleeps
though it has been known to take naps
have lapses in judgments
oppress
the very liberties
that gives it its zest
and makes millions
who make it millions
flock to its sidewalks and alleys
to walk along *grachten*
and see reflections of selves in waters

but this
is the place of freedom
and you strut confidently
negotiating space
relaxed…
your body flows
….smoothly
like the waters along the canals
rolls
sways….
dips….

HER(E)

glides along
to rhythms inspired by rainbows
on cold winter days

you are so sure of your ability to lead…
…even me?
and yet…
so unsure of your beauty and grace
you mistake looks of passersby
for curiosity or contempt
missing desire
refusing to acknowledge
lingering eyes…
longing
to draw you near
but resisting in fear…
not of you
but of selves
so they continue on
dying of thirst
rather than sip from waters
tinted pink
from red lights reflecting

dodging labels
you march on

conquering cultures
and districts
finding yourself
on your own terms
one step
one sweet step
one sweet rainbow step
at a time

some may call you
butch
stud
tomboy
dyke…
but
not us
not me

no, self-proclaimed
ranger androgyne
king/queen
go-d|is
i call you friend of mine

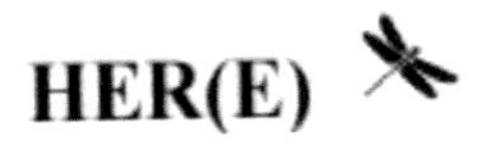

short stories

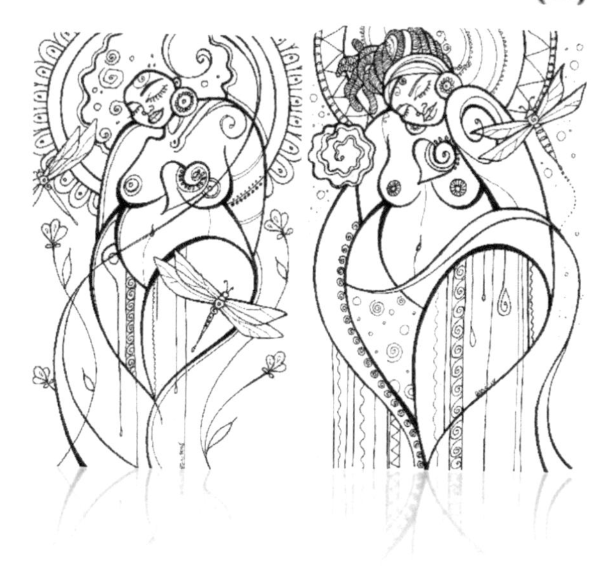

1. creation in rewrite

in the beginning, there was the go-d|is and the go-d|is became word. through words she gave birth to voice and called forth both the heavens and the earth; and she saw that these were good. then go-d|is called forth day and night, beheld their beauty and also saw that these were good. for several days she tirelessly continued her creations sounding out sea and land, winds and spirits; and she saw that these were also good. one-day go-d|is looked about and knew that while the earth was beautiful, it was barren and saw that while the heavens hummed with spirits. yet even as she marveled in her creation she knew that something was missing and so go-d|is called from the earth pairs of living beings; animals of all natures for the skies, the earth, and the sea and she saw that this was good.

still, the feeling of disappointment had not dissipated and as she looked about she realized that her spirits could still not fully experience her creation; and she knew, again, that this was not good. after much contemplation and searching within herself for answers she stretched out her hands upon her spirits and called forth within them hu(e)man(e) life. it was in this way that go-d|is created women in her own images and likenesses. there were all forms of women; in all quality of hues and complexions, all types of builds, speaking in all sorts of tongues and go-d|is looked about at this marvel and knew that this was indeed good.

these women, in experiencing the world, drew together and formed friendships, families, and communities. they created bonds between them, linking them each to others. some bonds deepened, and where and when this occurred these women spoke sacred words they called vows, claiming one for the other, above all others, and so they became partners in life and love. go-d|is, from beyond the earth and sky, acknowledged these unions and knew that they were good and for a time life went on as such.

the women honored go-d|is, respected the earth and sustained themselves through what they could gather from around them and more importantly from their friendships and unions. then one day they looked about and realized that there were more animals than before and they did not understand, for their own numbers had not multiplied. approaching go-d|is they asked why no more of their kind had been sent to them, but go-d|is did not respond. so, they set about studying the animals closely and saw that not only were there different species of animals, but that within one type there were two kinds; one which seemed like them, but another that was different. the women were shocked, for within their kind there were only ones like themselves. again they approached go-d|is and asked why there were differences between the animals; why there were some like them and some that were different, and again go-d|is gave no answer. they returned to their studies of the animals and they saw that amongst the animals there were also partnerships amongst the ones like them, but they also saw that there were unions between those that were like them and those that were not like them and they were puzzled. soon,

they saw that from these unions between those that were like them and those that were not like them more animals came; some that were like them and some that were not like them. now they understood why the animals were multiplying and they were not and again they approached go-d|is and asked why she had not created amongst their species beings that were not like them. go-d|is gave no answer.

the women then called together a great council of all the women who had scattered to all ends of the earth and those who understood explained what they knew to those who did not know. when everyone knew and understood there arose a great debate; some saying that go-d|is should be made to create some beings of their kind that were not like them and others who said the way it was and had always been was just fine. the council went on for many days and nights and finally those who knew explained that with the animals it seemed as if with the ones which were there from the beginning of time, something strange was happening. 'life leaves them,' they explained, 'and it does not return to their bodies, so that they are no more.' they further explained that the new ones thus replaced the older ones and so their kinds continued. 'this will not happen with us, unless there are new ones. we will not continue unless there are ones who are not like us. between us we are not making any more of us and so it is with the animals as well.' they explained again that even from the unions between them, which go-d|is had said were good, there could be no offspring. many again called for go-d|is to be made to create some that were not like them. 'our kind must continue, there must be more of us, there is so much yet to be experienced,' they said. many others did not agree and suggested instead that go-d|is be made to allow them to make more of their kind between them. the others argued that this was not the way and that go-d|is would not comply. then those who had wanted to make offspring between them decided that they would live without offspring, rather than have go-d|is introduce those not like their kind amongst them. and so a great schism was created between the

women. go-d|is, listening in, knew that this was not good, but did not intervene.

finally, the two camps made two very different decisions. the first went off together, leaving the others behind and continued their lives as they had always been living; from their births until their deaths in a continuum of women. the other group went in search of gpd|is and for days and nights on end beseeched her to send to them some that were of their kind, but who were not like them. at wits end go-d|is answered and said, 'this is the way i made you, in my images and likenesses, and i saw that it was good. this was only for a while, so that spirit could experience life through you. but you are not happy and it is your will that i create again and so i will, but all of this will change. are you ready for that?' the women all agreed that they were ready and willing to accept the changes for they wanted to multiply and again they begged of go-d|is that she create those that were of their kind, but not like them. go-d|is then explained that at the center of the earth, in the most beautiful garden, there was a fruit tree and if the women found and ate the fruits those who were of their kind, but not like them would be created. the women organized and sent out the smartest and the strongest amongst them. after a long journey they arrived at the center of the earth and beheld the tree with the most beautiful fruits. it almost hurt their eyes to view them and only the strong yearnings to have more of their kind stopped the women from becoming transfixed. suddenly an old, long, thick, lizard slithered down the tree's trunk and spoke. 'well, isn't this what you came for; this fruit, this freedom to procreate. eat it, be free and be immortal." and as they were looking at the lizard, looking older than any animal they had ever seen, another lizard appeared, just as old and just as brown and spotted and spoke as well. 'everything will change, you have been warned. you can all turn around now and return to your people or you can eat of this fruit and change your world. the choice is yours, but there is no going back once it has been changed and there is no coming back once you leave." one by one the women stepped forth and ate a fruit, some two and three and when they were satisfied, at the snakes' coaxing they took barrels back for the women they had left behind. and go-d|is saw that they had chosen and sent forth her spirits and created men amongst them and the women were happy. they quickly formed unions women with men and the species multiplied.

however, there remained within this group woman in unions with other women, who had not left with the others and when the multiplying began they were happy, and no longer sad, and when babies were unwanted or orphaned they stepped in to raise these between them. there were also women who partnered with men for a time and then returned to their women with babies in tow. amongst the men there were also men in union with men and they too raised babies between them when the occasions arose. and for a while all was happy and go-d|is, from beyond, looked about and saw that this was good.

but the day came when the men who did not know how it was before began to question the leadership of the women and the purpose of those who could not multiply and while the women tried to explain how it was in the beginning the men were not convinced. they said the purpose of people was to reproduce. it was the goal of the species to survive and those who could not help with its survival by multiplying were not needed and should be cast out. the women at first pleaded for understanding, but as time went on some began to wonder if the argument was not sound. between the men and women who partnered together it was agreed that unions should be between men and women only and sent out from amongst them all those who wished to partner with their own kind and speak the sacred vows. many who wanted to stay amongst them absolved their unions and partnered with those that were not like them. women who loved women partnered with men and men who loved men partnered with women or they stayed alone. however, in secret, many still gathered together and loved each other, but did not speak its name. and so it came that who they were and what they did became invisible.

those who chose to be together publicly were ridiculed and sent out or set apart, until it became a great shame for two of the same to love each other. and as it was in the beginning, it was no more. go-d|is looked about and saw that this was not good, but she did not intervene. instead she continued to reach out to the heart of each woman and each man, both those who loved their own kind and those that loved the other kind and tried to make each see that they were all perfect in their own right.

then, the day came when those who loved their own kind were no longer willing to be shamed and shunned and they began to speak out and make themselves visible. they recalled stories they had heard about how it had been before and they knew that they were beautiful. they fought for their rights and their (re)memory and go-d|is looked on from beyond and saw that this was good. the fight for their rights took many, many years and was not without causalities. and the women and the men who loved their own kind called upon go-d|is to strengthen them and make strong their hearts and minds to reason with those who seemed unreasonable, those who would do them harm. and go-d|is strengthened them. they traveled to the place where the first women who had left the group had settled and there erected a temple in their honor. from there they studied and researched and prayed and continued conversation with those who opposed them. until one day the two camps convened a council of their best scholars. they debated long into the nights and deep into the days. those against them said that it was unnatural and most important against go-d|is. they reminded them that even in nature there were animals who attached themselves to their own kind in their species and more importantly go-d|is herself had created them this way. in the end the council deliberated and decided that everyone was entitled to freedoms and that the sacred vows could once again be performed between those women and men who loved their own kind. and a peace settled between the camps. go-d|is, from beyond and within, looked about and said that this was very good indeed.

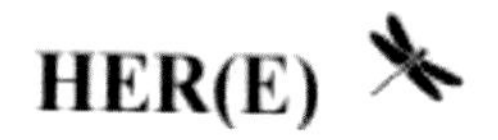

2. daughters

they say that right at the moment i was born, down to the very second, the sun disappeared and the wind screamed so loud that some said they could hear the wails of the ancestors in it. the son had not been born. it would not have been remarkable except that there were clouds in the sky that day and my father, it is said, wept bitter tears for three days and then bought a case of johnny walker and sent it to the bushman. whether because the earth had tasted his tears and enjoyed their salt or because it was simply time for the rains to come, it had begun to pour and people say that the water that gathered in their cisterns and drums had been too salty to drink. they say it rained straight for a month causing rocks to crash from mountains blocking roads and isolating villagers. there was no party to welcome me to the community and because of this, i received no name for 60 days while the island recovered from the downpour and my father recovered from his grief. but they say when the rains stopped he took to the mountains and spilled seeds alone for a week wishing that he could empty himself so that he would have no more. still, there would be more, as there had been so many before me. the villagers had believed that he could endure no more disappointments, but each time when he had recovered, he would try again. it was his mission, his purpose for being, even after he had replaced my mother twice and banished her daughters from him as he had banished the daughters before them as well. that is the beginning of the story that followed me off my island and onto the next one where i was sent for my own good it was said. even people who believed themselves to be non-superstitious stayed clear of me. they would warn their children and grandchildren that strange things happened around people who could send the sun into hiding. my grandmother though assured me that that the sun had been only taking a break and said i should not worry because the animals had seen nothing wrong with my birth. she said they had not howled, bleated or brayed and said if they had that then i would have had to watch out, because then the bad spirits would have been walking with me. but the animals had sung no strange songs for me and so i was free to grow.

the birth had been normal otherwise; there had been no navel string around my neck, no caul on my face and i had come out headfirst. it was just another, normal birth and another disappointment for my father in a long list of disappointments - 17 to be exact. therefore, it had only been different in that there had been no sun and he had gotten no son.

they say if he had acted differently then maybe the next one would have been a boy, but he had behaved so badly throughout the rains and in the mountains, cursing at the skies and ripping at his skin that he had been punished. they said the ancestors must have thought that he was cursing them and so the father who wanted just one son, would have none. instead, he would have 20 daughters and only their bastard boys to carry his name. the husband who had wanted one wife would have five, sacrificing one after the other in the desperate pursuit of his boy, his heir. we were all fatherless daughters; children with families, but no papa. perhaps that explains why none of us would marry. why none of us would anchor ourselves to the whims of husbands, of men.

my oldest sister had laughed so hard on the day i was born that they say she had been left with a permanent smile on her face. this was ok, though since it had only added to her beauty. she had laughed in my father's face and even after he had slapped her to the floor, the nurses said, she laughed on, jumping up and running outside where her laughter had caused her down there to cry. she never spoke again, though whenever she saw our father laughter cascaded from her throat and her tears flowed from down there. she would birth the first grandson and laughed even when she allowed her shiftless lover to give the boy her father's name. my sister after her had not laughed through any of it, but had stood silently by in the waiting room listening to the sounds of her third mother, praying that she would finally have what it took. when the sky turned dark she had known that whatever her mother had had it had not been enough. she left the island after the rains, tired of waiting for the son that would change him and allow all of their lives to get better. her sons would all carry his name, but would never see his face, not one single one. she had banished him as he had banished her and while she could forgive him, she could not allow her sons to become for him the enough she and her sisters had never been. my third oldest sister had sat hunched on her heels for three hours smoking one mentholated kool after the next. she swears that the sun glowed red just before it disappeared. she thinks it meant that i was born lucky or as lucky as i could be with a father that didn't want another daughter. she wanted me from the start though and took me under her wing. people say that her face doesn't match her body and have called her a bulldyke; the soft beauty contrasting with the hardness of mass and muscles, but i still think that she is perfect. one day i heard a lady *call her out her name*, but only once, because when she tried to say it again she never got past bull. she told me she secretly liked the word, but she couldn't let the lady try to embarrass her like that or others would follow. needless to say until now no one else has. some say she's brick, but i've seen her cry enough to know that she's cotton. through a friend at the census office she managed to have more success at breeding women than our father did and had three sons who carried her name or his name through her. there was nothing remarkable about sisters 5, 6, and 7, except that they were triplets and so he had been trebly disappointed. they said he drank himself into a stupor for 3 weeks, one for each daughter and when he was sober again marched wife #1 to court and replaced her with wife #2. she had not been brilliant but he had loved her and had promised her forever at the set price of a son. she had given it six unsuccessful attempts before duty was done and she succumbed to the pressure and fatigue of too many babies in too short a time. but it was probably the knowledge that the birth of another daughter had ensured that the woman he already had in mind would replace her. he married my mother within three weeks and 6 months, 3 weeks and 2 days to the day of their wedding sybille was born. the nurses said that she came into the world screaming his name and the midwife almost dropped her. some say it was her come again, but he paid neither them nor her any mind and even while she silently followed his movements through eyes which were a brilliant grey, but could not see, he pursued his dream of a son. her calls for his attention went unanswered and he merely sent her away when her look turned too knowing, too familiar, causing him to feel as if he was under a pressure to prove something to a spirit long gone. he knew that from the start she pitied him for his trying; his trying too hard. he had left the church and taken my mother with him by the time she became pregnant again. this time the bush doctor had promised a son and with all his being he believed him. so she had risen early every morning and picked fresh leaves from 3 different plants, put them in hot water to draw and boiled the concoction until it bubbled. she said that she had had no taste buds until she had become pregnant. every day he had been optimistic and had prayed to the ancestors to deliver the son he so desired. when my mother went into labor on the eve of a major hurricane he began to worry and when he was told that my sixteenth sister was born the devastation he felt matched that of the island. some said he walked around for days dazed by the fact that his house had survived, while his hope was slowly dying. because he was getting bitter at this point he named her simon, but mother managed to add an e to the name while the census official distracted him with 'next time's'. the bush doctor said that sons needed to be cooked up differently and for the first time in years my father tried to remember that he could actually make love to a wife. they said he became a romantic, wooing mother with roses and poems. had his older daughters cook dinners of plantain, shrimps, conches, salmon, goat, snapper, avocado, dumpling, rice and peas and more. she grew plump under his attention, but she also grew scared. she too visited the bush doctor, or so they say, and every month until she became pregnant on the first morning of her menses she went into the trees beyond the yard and gave her blood to the earth. he had told her this would appease the spirits which had been plaguing her husband and would make sure the next baby would be a son. she had believed him, in part because she wanted to keep her husband, but also because she knew her body could carry no more babies safely after this. she said when she became pregnant she knew i was a girl, but still hoped differently. she started making plans to leave the island for the bigger one where she could join her mother, just in

case. she had smiled along with him when he chose names again and again. it would be this time and so this time was more special than any other. he had added on to the house again, marshaled the help of the daughters he had not wanted and prepared a small castle for his son. she had scrimped together every penny she could find and on the day she went into labor her account finally registered enough money for her to move with her four daughters and not be a burden on her mother. she had wept when she felt her first pains and closed the fresh, new blue bedroom behind her. my mother had walked alone to the hospital and sent the sisters to find their father. so they say she had seemed in good spirits, smiling with everyone she met along the way. she told me that the smiling had managed to mask the fact that inside she was already saying her goodbyes. each face was one she was not expecting to see much longer after my birth. when the rains stopped she took the four of us and made way to the big island. he was not very unhappy to see us go and within weeks had taken up with yet another woman who he would make his fourth wife. she would have neither the luck nor the inclination for many attempts and after bearing two daughters, died at an age younger than my father's eldest daughter. it was only then that my mother was sent for again. he had needed someone to take care of his compound and my mother had fallen onto bad luck on the big island. so she packed us up and with my grandmother returned to him. she had made clear that she would make no more babies with him and settled in and around his life as something else; a sister almost. there, under the watchful eyes of my older sisters the young ones, including i, grew up focused on school and on making something of ourselves that could make him proud. but, his pride eluded us. even me, the brightest and best they said, who would leave the island and return a doctor, bullish in the same ways my favorite sister was, lucky in love with two beautiful sons, just in time to see his last wife bear him one child, neither boy nor girl, or maybe both. they had rushed the baby, the mother and my mother to the neighboring town so that the special doctors there could decide what x would become. however, it would not be enough for him or maybe that

was enough for him. in an act of final madness, they say, he cut his wrists and bled a trail from the houses he had shared with his different wives, that he had left for his doctor daughter in order to care for his family, to the hills where he had spilled seed long years before. perhaps, i thought, when i heard i had been left a compound full of daughters, i had not been so lucky after all. and when the news of his passing finally reached my mother and his last wife, they were told that he had been borne to his final resting place on the shoulders of his daughters and they had decided that no decision needed to be made on that day for the last of his babies. eighteen years after the death of our father, that baby – his only son - was registered as male in the island's registry and my sisters and i threw a celebration worthy of his arrival.

Author Acknowledgement

This book, which has been at least 10 years in the making, would not have been possible without the support of the following people:

Dr. Maria van Enckevort, my head editor who took a very, very, very rough manuscript, brought order to it, and then went through it several more times with me bringing improved structure and flow with each read over. Thank you Juffrouw, for seeing the potential of my book, believing in my dream and offering your time and energy for guidance, Eye, I & i am great filled for you;

My unofficial team of co-editors Lisa Pourier, Xiarella Lewis, Denise Vijber, and Rene Violenus for going through the early drafts and making comments and suggestions. Your support is appreciated more than you will ever know. Peepee Lou, for the sharp eyes and encouragement for a decade and more, thank you;

Lincoln Charles for creating the drafts of the concepts of the beautiful artwork for the front and back covers and for always being up to doing my graphic work when called upon. Thanks lil bro bro;

Lionel Charles for taking care of my dogs and cat on those occasions when I needed a break to regroup; Thanks to you too lil bro;

Clara Reyes for providing me with platform after platform over the years from which I could present my poetry and develop my voice. Moreover, of course, for always also for being a muse, mentor and often my mediator and voice of reason in the sadder seasons. Words can never be enough;

Danielle Boodoo – Fortune, the illustrator of the artwork inside the book and on the front cover. You jumped right in to this project, when I slid into your DM to ask about your artwork, and created four amazing pieces that reflect different parts of me and one amazing cover to tie it all together. Thanks eternally;

Alston Lourens for having a go at layout for me. In a world full of horses thanks for consistently being a unicorn who comes to my aid;

To the people who have supported my poetry over the years whether it was in audiences or via social media, your encouragement was and is most appreciated and I thank you all;

To my mother and grandmother, Elka & Carmen, for their unwavering support, their openness and the space created for me in which I could be unapologetically, unashamedly, unrepentantly, unembarrassedly me, Thank you, Thank you, Thank you;

To my family and friends who have supported my writing, my events, my passion – your support was and is appreciated and you are too numerous to mention, but here is a go, Tracy, Evy, Sinfra, Vonti, Danielle, LaRonda, Denotra, Annette, Rene, Kerine, Asha, Tina,

HER(E)

Silvy, Arlette, Cassandra, Rene, Mosera, Lisa, Tamya, Angelica, if I left anyone out, you are in my heart;

To the women who have been a part of my life whether fleetingly or more long term, who were lov(h)ers and/or loves, Pookie, Big D, Jay, SistaFruit, Wially, Aix, SaS, SuperGirl, SR, Hun, Caddy, Aix, for at some point in my life being the apple of my eye and my muse(s) - Eye, I & i thank you;

To you dushi, for supporting me throughout this year and a half as I worked on this book, for being my cheerleader, my sparring partner, my pusher – MSB4R, may our paths always lead us back towards each other;

To my GirlPrince, Tianna, aka Tounky, aka Tounks, aka Tounka Tita, aka Tita, aka SocaT, for raising me… and teaching me so much more than I ever thought I had to learn, for humbling me and teaching me to be in awe of the smallest things, for inspiring me to be better and braver and bolder, so that you can one day also be all of those things also and so much more, I thank you for *longing* to me and I wish for you a more open, safe and beautiful world, whoever you become;

Finally to all my nieces, and my nephews, my dawtas and suns (both biologically and spiritually) that you may always have the confidence to hear the beat of your own drumming and then dance to it, sing to it, chant to it, and that you always, regardless of your own sexual orientation always create safe space(s) for people to be their full selves in your presence.

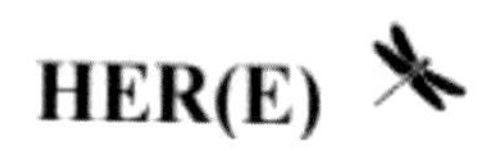

Amandla Awethu!!!
Until Victory is Ours!!!
Until We are ALL Free!!!

Each on her/his own journey, without judgment or interference, unless otherwise requested and then with detachment. – GoddessEyeism

Made in the USA
Columbia, SC
22 June 2020

11781806R00075